Summary of

A Mind of Your Own

The Truth About Depression and How Women
Can Heal Their Bodies to Reclaim Their Lives

by Kelly Brogan, MD with Kristin Loberg

Instaread

Please Note

This is a summary with analysis.

Table of Contents

Overview

A Mind of Your Own, by holistic women's health psychiatrist Kelly Brogan, aims to help women better understand the root causes of depression and the pervasive myths surrounding antidepressants. Brogan encourages readers to take their health and well being into their own hands. She outlines a four-week protocol of dietary restrictions, adjustments to sleep and exercise, and meditation. This regimen is intended to provide women with a healthier alternative to antidepressants. By taking an empowered, proactive approach to health, women can overcome debilitating symptoms, become healthier, and ultimately thrive without antidepressants.

Over the course of years as a traditional psychiatrist, Brogan prescribed antidepressants to women because she believed that a chemical imbalance in the brain accounted for mental health disorders. A health crisis of her own forced Brogan to reconsider the conventional wisdom surrounding pharmaceutical treatments for common ailments. After being diagnosed with Hashimoto's thyroiditis, an autoimmune disease, shortly after giving birth to her first child, Brogan began researching her illness. She discovered that her condition often went undiagnosed as the cause of depression.

To treat her condition without medication, Brogan investigated alternative means of healing. With the help of a naturopathic doctor, she learned that her thyroid dysfunction was caused by a combination of postpartum bodily changes, an imbalance in her gut, and poor dietary choices. Brogan took her newfound knowledge and passion and applied it to patients suffering from depression with astoundingly positive results.

Aggressive marketing from pharmaceutical companies has helped perpetuate a myth that depression, anxiety, and other mental health disorders are attributable to a chemical imbalance. However, no study has ever actually proven this theory. Pharmaceutical companies have much to gain monetarily from this unsubstantiated claim. They have manipulated and even suppressed studies that suggest that the causes of depression and related symptoms of inflammation are not adequately treated by antidepressants. As a result, doctors overlook the undeniable link between gut health and brain health.

The key to mental and physical health is allowing the body to heal naturally by addressing inflammation, which is a major cause of many illnesses including depression. Instead of blindly buying into the notion that pills will be an overnight cure, women can trust their own bodies and their bodies' innate healing wisdom.

Important People

Kelly Brogan is a psychiatrist who specializes in women's mental health. She is the co-author of *Integrative Therapies for Depression* (2015).

Kristin Loberg is a writer and has co-authored several *New York Times* bestsellers, including *Grain Brain* (2013) with David Perlmutter and *The End of Illness* (2012) with David Agus.

Key Takeaways

1. Depression is not the result of a serotonin deficiency. Depression is a signal that the body is adapting to a stressor.

2. Pharmaceutical companies have shamelessly suppressed and manipulated data about the efficacy of antidepressants.

3. Other medications, not just antidepressants, can trigger symptoms of depression.

4. Overreliance on medication can actually harm the body's natural ability to restore balance and health.

5. Learning about the interconnectedness of the bodily systems can help you support optimal immune functioning, inducing more vibrant health than prescription drugs can.

6. The link between gut health and brain health is vital to overall well being.

7. Inflammation is the primary cause of depression and other chronic diseases including cancer.

8. The most important step in recovering a natural state of health is making major dietary shifts, which will have a beneficial effect on the microbiome in as little as 72 hours.

9. The dietary protocol for taking charge of mental health requires eliminating gluten, dairy, and sugar.

10. A genetic predisposition to illness, including symptoms of depression, doesn't have to determine health. Addressing environmental factors can profoundly improve well being regardless of genetic makeup.

11. In addition to taking supplements and embracing an anti-inflammatory diet, prioritize regular exercise and meditation, making them life-long habits.

Thank you for purchasing this Instaread book

**Download the Instaread mobile app to get
unlimited text & audio summaries
of bestselling books.**

Visit Instaread.co
to learn more.

Analysis

Key Takeaway 1

Depression is not the result of a serotonin deficiency. Depression is a signal that the body is adapting to a stressor.

Analysis

Pharmaceutical companies spent $4.53 billion in advertising in 2014. They claim that depression is due to an imbalance in the brain of serotonin, a neurotransmitter, and present antidepressants as the antidote to depression. Yet depression has never been proven to be the result of a neurological chemical imbalance. Instead, it is the result of the body's interrelated systems attempting to adapt to stressors, such as inflammation.

The notion that depression is "an illness of the mind," as Andrew Solomon writes in *The Noonday Demon: An Atlas of Depression,* is a pervasive one. [1] Adding to this confusion, cultural myths about depression have drama-tized and obscured its causes. From a medical perspective, the romantic association of depression with creativity is particularly distracting. Writers throughout history have documented its ravaging effects on their lives, including twentieth-century women writers, such as Virginia Woolf, Sylvia Plath, Anne Sexton, and Alejandra Pizarnik, who all committed suicide. Although readers may find solace in reading about the experiences of others who share their symptoms, the cultural trope of the tortured artist does nothing to illuminate the causes of depression: dis-tressed body systems.

The symptoms of depression, including foggy mind and profound sadness, can often be so encompassing that it's difficult for those experiencing it to think about anything else beyond their own malaise and suffering, let alone consider and evaluate its potential causes. Moreover, a social stigma still adheres to mental health disorders as if they reflect the personal failings of the people suffering from them. This stigma contributes to a culture of shame in which individuals who suffer from depression do not question the doctors prescribing the medication because they are desperate for a quick and relatively private fix.

Key Takeaway 2

Pharmaceutical companies have shamelessly suppressed and manipulated data about the efficacy of antidepressants.

Analysis

The pharmaceutical industry sponsors 70 percent of the studies conducted on antidepressants. Pharmaceutical companies are heavily invested in suppressing any evidence that antidepressants do not improve patients' lives. In fact, medication can often lead to a worsening of symptoms over time and rarely facilitates true healing. Many studies have shown that antidepressants are no more effective than a placebo.

Psychiatrist David Healy, author of *Pharmageddon* (2012), has been critical of medical colleagues who don't stand up to corporate interests even in the face of damning evidence. He writes, "Doctors keep patients on lots of drugs, even if they are uncomfortable with it. And if you ask them why they're doing so, the answer you'll get is: 'Well, this is the standard of care, and if I don't take care of it this way, I'm going to be in awful trouble.'" [2]

For physicians with qualms about prescribing antidepressants, or who at least wish to prescribe them less frequently, the question is a moral one. No one knows the long-term effects of taking these drugs. They have been shown to have an adverse effect on adolescents in particular. In all age groups, these drugs sometimes have triggered violent episodes. A number of high-profile shootings in the United States have been linked to antidepressant use, most notably the Wakefield massacre in 2000, in which Michael McDermott shot and killed seven co-workers. In the weeks leading up to the shooting, McDermott had tripled his dosage of Prozac, causing some to infer a correlation between the antidepressants and his criminal behavior. [3] Given the potentially violent consequences, it's willfully ignorant for Big Pharma to aggressively promote these products while suppressing their potentially negative effects.

Key Takeaway 3

Other medications, not just antidepressants, can trigger symptoms of depression.

Analysis

Antidepressants can worsen depression symptoms, causing a cascade effect of subsequent diagnoses and more prescriptions. Many people feel worse, not better, when their serotonin levels are boosted. Other types of medication outside the antidepressant classification can also cause depressive symptoms. For example, antacids can cause a deficiency in Vitamin B_{12}, an enzyme that is critical for gut health. An imbalanced gut can trigger depression.

Consider a young woman with risk factors for depression, such as high stress levels and genetic predisposition. Even nonprescription drugs could send her into a spiral of depression. Focused on emotional stressors, such as a failing relationship or unsteady job, she is likely unaware of how Tylenol can dampen emotion and contribute to depression or of how birth control pills, which suppress hormones, might contribute to her depression by interfering with the body's natural processes. Unfortunately, this lack of awareness drives her further into the throes of her mental health disorder. Since many sufferers of depression report self-absorption, she might have more negative thoughts about herself because she's aware that she's not functioning in social settings, or life, as well as she normally does. Her experience is a common one and exemplifies the need for women to have better education about how their bodies function in reaction to medicines.

Key Takeaway 4

Overreliance on medication can actually harm the body's natural ability to restore balance and health.

Analysis

The body is designed to heal itself. If a person scrapes a leg, for example, the body knows innately what it needs to do to repair any cellular damage and protect the tissue below the epidermis. [4] Mental health disorders are, like scrapes, conditions of the body; as with physical health, the body is capable of healing itself. A skilled clinician can help to guide women to mental wellness, but no pill can replace personal accountability for spiritual, psychological, and physiological health.

The field of mind-body medicine is predicated on the notion that our minds are intimately connected to our bodies. Dr. Lissa Rankin, author of *Mind Over Medicine: Scientific Proof That You Can Heal Yourself* (2013), has studied this phenomenon. As a traditional Western doctor, she came across studies that proved the powerful role the mind plays in healing. [5] Given this connection, she began to wonder if certain physical symptoms are somehow a manifestation of an emotional wound or pathology.

Numerous anecdotes and personal accounts suggest that Rankin is not alone in her belief. Consider the case of Anita Moorjani, who fell into a coma after a four-year battle with lymphoma. To the surprise of her doctors, she woke up and had a spontaneous remission. Moorjani had a near-death experience while she was comatose that prompted her to stay alive and to live without fear. [6] Such epiphanies are less likely to happen if women are continually looking to Western medicine as an authority over their own intuition. Women know their own bodies best, and this intimate knowledge shouldn't be discounted because a doctor says so.

Key Takeaway 5

Learning about the interconnectedness of the bodily systems can help you support optimal immune functioning, inducing more vibrant health than prescription drugs can.

Analysis

The field of psychoneuroimmunology examines the relationships between the gut, the brain, and the immune system. Attention to the ways in which these systems are intricately interrelated will support an individual's mental health.

With respect to depression, traditional psychiatrists are primarily concerned with the brain and only the brain. Rarely do they look at other physiological markers, such as blood pressure, thyroid function, and blood sugar levels. Over the last several years, however, patients and physicians alike have become more aware of the link between certain foods and mental health. Dr. James Greenblatt, author of *The Breakthrough Depression Solution* (2011), saw a patient who was on three different medications, for anxiety, depression, and ADHD. The patient wasn't getting any better and was having trouble sleeping. Instead of prescribing a sleep aid at the patient's request, Greenblatt ran tests and discovered that the patient had a severe gluten intolerance, which is now widely known to induce mood swings. [7]

Key Takeaway 6

The link between gut health and brain health is vital to overall well being.

Analysis

Researchers have recently discovered a lymphatic system in the brain whose primary purpose is to connect with the immune system. However, today's antidepressants were formulated without the understanding of the connection between the brain and the gut. They aren't designed for holistic functioning and well being.

Over the last few years, the health media has helped to popularize the notion of the gut as "the second brain." [8] Researchers have made great strides to better understand the actual mechanisms at work and have looked at how this link affects different populations. For example, in a study of autistic children, approximately 75 percent of the children were found to have difficulty with their gastrointestinal (GI) system. [9] Conventional medicine doctors would not recommend that parents of autistic children treat them via diet and supplements to strengthen the GI tract. But based on this budding field of knowledge, it just might be the treatment that is most effective. Similarly, a young mother might be unaware of the connection between diet and depression. She might believe that her rapidly shifting emotions are due to her personal failing or her inability to manage her children and not recognize that the pancakes she had for breakfast were to blame.

Key Takeaway 7

Inflammation is the primary cause of depression and other chronic diseases including cancer.

Analysis

Inflammation plays an essential role in the body's immunity; it helps the body protect itself against potentially dangerous agents, such as environmental pollutants. Yet inflammatory agents also have a direct effect on brain function. When inflammation becomes a chronic condition, cells can be damaged leading to the development of diseases. Cytokines, which are markers of inflammation, are elevated in those suffering from depression.

Rudolf Virchow, a nineteenth-century German pathologist, was the first to study the role of inflammation in disease development, believing that illness began at the cellular level. [10] Thanks to Virchow's early investigations, it's now commonly accepted that chronic inflammation can have deadly consequences. In the health and wellness markets, enterprising nutritionists and physicians have been capitalizing on the trend toward anti-inflammatory diets. Dr. Andrew Weil, a trusted Dr. Oz-sanctioned holistic health doctor, counts an anti-inflammatory diet as high on his list of tips for living a healthy life. [11] Some inflammatory conditions, such as rheumatoid arthritis, are known precursors to cancer. Thus, in addition to addressing symptoms of depression, anti-inflammatory diets help with a multitude of other illnesses.

Key Takeaway 8

The most important step in recovering a natural state of health is making major dietary shifts, which will have a beneficial effect on the microbiome in as little as 72 hours.

Analysis

The microbiome, a collection of trillions of microorganisms that reside in the body, has an important impact on overall health by helping to digest food, absorb nutrients, and support the immune system. When the microbiome is out of balance, meaning the gut bacteria is disrupted, it can cause illness.

Dr. Mark Hyman, the director of the Cleveland Clinic for Functional Medicine, is one of the most enthusiastic adopters of the food-as-medicine movement. He is an expert in the field of nutrigenomics, which explores food as agents that interact with our genes for better or worse. When the food is whole, healthy, and life-sustaining, the interaction of nutrients with human genetic expression produces ameliorative effects. [12]

Fortunately, thanks to food activism, a movement based on eating whole, healthy foods, people are becoming exposed to the benefits of eating locally sourced fare. Alice Waters, a California-based restaurateur and organic food enthusiast, has been pushing better nutrition in schools for decades. Waters's approach combats depression from a roundabout angle. If children and adults are overweight, this increases their likelihood of suffering from depression. [13] Therefore, educating children about nutrition at an early age can improve their overall wellness, including their mental health.

Key Takeaway 9

The dietary protocol for taking charge of mental health requires eliminating gluten, dairy, and sugar.

Analysis

Though it might sound drastic, the foundation of an anti-inflammatory dietary program is the elimination of gluten, sugar, and dairy. Gluten can permeate the intestinal tract, leading to leaky gut syndrome, in which the pores of the GI tract widen and allow toxins and food particles to slip into the bloodstream. This prompts the immune system to go into defensive mode by producing inflammation. Most dairy will lead to inflammation; for example, exomes in cow's milk promote the production of cytokines, markers of inflammation. A blood sugar imbalance is a major contributing factor to depression.

If a young woman has been persistently restless, fatigued, and melancholy for weeks, she might seek an explanation for what has changed within her. She might first consider the season; does she have the winter blues? Or perhaps she has been emotionally devastated since her grandmother died. She might try to speak with a therapist or confide in a well-meaning friend about her problems. But unless those individuals are conscious of the impact of nutrition on mental health, the young woman will continue to overlook her diet. Even if she consults doctors, the likelihood that they will suggest she first try a dietary intervention is slim, and therefore, the possibility of healing through her food choices is less likely to occur.

Nonetheless, many people attest that they have cured their depressive tendencies with food. Food blogger Rachael Abel suffered from depression and anxiety since childhood, but it wasn't until she decided to take total control of her well being, starting with a "no excuses" rule, that she came around to cutting out dairy, sugar, and gluten. Now, she reports that she is not only happy but "ecstatically happy." [14] Her blog, *Love Yourself Green*, offers inspiration for those who need motivation and anecdotal evidence that eating more cleanly can alter moods in a positive way.

Key Takeaway 10

A genetic predisposition to illness, including symptoms of depression, doesn't have to determine health. Addressing environmental factors can profoundly improve well being, regardless of genetic makeup.

Analysis

Past is not prologue when it comes to a family history of mental health disorders. By changing daily habits, including diet and exercise regimens, individuals can positively affect the way their genes express themselves.

One prominent example of this is the experience of actress Mariel Hemingway, who documented her family's history with mental illness in *Running From Crazy*, a documentary film about her ancestral legacy of mood disorders. Most famously, Ernest Hemingway, her grandfather, was an alcoholic who committed suicide. To escape this aspect of her familial DNA, she adopted a strict regimen of healthy eating, yoga, and meditation. She is the author of an organic cookbook and believes wholeheartedly in eating to stabilize mood. [15] Hemingway is living proof that no one's fate is absolutely predetermined by their genetic makeup.

Key Takeaway 11

In addition to taking supplements and embracing an anti-inflammatory diet, prioritize regular exercise and meditation, making them lifelong habits.

Analysis

While diet may be the most important component to mood stability, mediation, exercise, and rest have also been shown to improve and ameliorate mental health symptoms.

Exercise and meditation are widely known to support mental health. In a 2014 study, Dr. Madhav Goyal of Johns Hopkins School of Medicine found that even meditation practitioners with minimal training could see large improvements in anxiety, depression, and pain. [16] Exercise can act as an inoculation against depression. [17] People are becoming aware that the daily decisions they make can have a huge impact on their well being. This raised awareness is the subject of *Thrive*, a 2014 book by Arianna Huffington, founder of *The Huffington Post*. Huffington extols the virtues of self-care including rest. To make the most out of sleep's restorative benefits, Huffington recommends adding one extra hour of sleep every day. She also suggests avoiding the use of electronics at least one hour before bedtime. [18]

Author's Style

Kelly Brogan and Kristin Loberg have written a detailed, highly informative take on the link between brain health, depression, and environmental factors including diet, exercise, and stress reduction. They describe the historical context of antidepressants and cite studies on the efficacies of antidepressants, building a case against the use of mental health pharmaceuticals.

Brogan and Loberg rely on hard science to prove their points about the biological and physiological roots of mental health disorders. They make it clear that the best thing a woman can do to take charge of her life is to start questioning and researching her current practices. This requires a reexamination of what's in her medicine cabinet and in her beauty regimen. Brogan uses her own personal experience with health empowerment to inspire readers. The closing sentiments reflect a spiritual slant on what it means to be a woman and advocate for women's health.

Author's Perspective

Kelly Brogan is board certified in psychiatry, integrative holistic medicine, and psychosomatic medicine, which is concerned with social, psychological, and behavioral elements of health. She practiced traditional psychiatry for years, prescribing medication including antidepressants for patients whose moods and energy levels had become seemingly pathological. Her turn to a holistic approach was dramatic and followed from her own health crisis. From her passionate, methodical treatment of this topic, she is evidently sincere in wanting to help women become educated and live better lives.

Kristin Loberg is a professional author with more than 15 years of experience in helping experts, particularly in the field of health, make their ideas accessible for a lay audience.

~~~~ END OF INSTAREAD ~~~~

Thank you for purchasing this Instaread book

**Download the Instaread mobile app to get
unlimited text & audio summaries
of bestselling books.**

Visit Instaread.co
to learn more.

References

1. Solomon, Andrew. *The Noonday Demon: An Atlas of Depression.* New York: Scribner, 2015, p. 20.

2. Straus, Tamara. "Meet the Doctor Big Pharma Can't Shut Up." *Alternet.* September 25, 2014. Accessed May 5, 2016. http://www.alternet. org/drugs/meet-doctor-big-pharma-cant-shut

3. Corbett, James. "Medicated to Death: SSRIs and Mass Killings." *The Corbett Report.* April 17, 2014. Accessed May 5, 2016. https://www.corbettreport. com/medicated-to-death-ssris-and-mass-killings/

4. Bushak, Lecia. "The 4-Stage Process Of Wound Healing." *Medical Daily.* November 15, 2014. Accessed May 5, 2016. http://www.medical-daily.com/4-stage-process-wound-healing-making-skin-stronger-310872

5. Rankin, Lissa. *Mind Over Medicine: Scientific Proof You Can Heal Yourself.* Carlsbad, CA: Hay House, 2013, p. 6.

6. Moorjani, Anita. *Dying to Be Me: My Journey from Cancer, to Near Death, to True Healing.* Carlsbad, CA: Hay House, 2012, pp. 3-6.

7. Greenblatt, James. "Is Gluten Making You Depressed?" *Psychology Today.* May 24, 2011. Accessed May 6, 2016. https://www.

psychologytoday.com/blog/the-break-through-depression-solution/201105/is-gluten-making-you-depressed

8. Wolkin, Jennifer. "Meet Your Second Brain: The Gut." *Mindful*. August 14, 2015. Accessed May 6, 2016. http://www.mindful.org/meet-your-second-brain-the-gut/

9. Kohn, David. "When Gut Bacteria Changes Brain Function." *The Atlantic Monthly*. June 24, 2015. Accessed May 6, 2016. http://www.theatlantic.com/health/archive/2015/06/gut-bacteria-on-the-brain/395918/

10. Heidland, A., et al. "The contribution of Rudolf Virchow to the concept of inflammation: what is still of importance?" *Journal of Nephrology*. May-June 2006. Accessed May 25, 2016. http://www.ncbi.nlm.nih.gov/pubmed/16874721

11. Woods, Sean. "Dr. Andrew Weil's Life Advice." *Men's Journal*. January 5, 2015. Accessed May 25, 2016. http://www.mensjournal.com/magazine/dr-andrew-weils-life-advice-20150105

12. Hyman, Mark. "Eat Your Medicine: Food as Pharmacology." *DrHyman.com*. April 3, 2013. Accessed May 6, 2016. http://drhyman.com/blog/2011/10/14/eat-your-medicine-food-as-pharmacology/

13. Finz, Stacy. "Alice Waters' Push for Local, Organic Setting National Agenda." *SF Gate.* May 9, 2010. Accessed May 25, 2016. http://www.sfgate.com/food/article/Alice-Waters-push-for-local-organic-setting-3189190.php

14. Abel, Rachael. "My Anxiety and Depression Disappeared When I Wasn't Even Looking." *Love Yourself Green.* February 6, 2015. Accessed May 9, 2016. http://www.loveyourselfgreen.com/2015/02/my-anxiety-and-depression-disappeared-when-i-wasnt-even-looking/

15. Fortini, Amanda. "The Importance of Not Being Ernest." *New York Times Magazine.* October 24, 2013. Accessed May 9, 2016. http://www.nytimes.com/2013/10/27/magazine/the-importance-of-not-being-ernest.html

16. Aubrey, Allison. "Mindfulness Meditation Can Help Relieve Anxiety and Depression." *Shots: Health News from NPR.* January 7, 2014. Accessed May 9, 2016. http://www.npr.org/sections/health-shots/2014/01/07/260470831/mindfulness-meditation-can-help-relieve-anxiety-and-depression

17. Reynolds, Gretchen. "How Exercise May Protect Against Depression." *The New York Times.* October 1, 2014. Accessed May 9, 2016. http://well.blogs.nytimes.com/2014/10/01/how-exercise-may-protect-against-depression/

18. Caprino, Kathy. "Four Life-Changing Concepts Arianna Huffington Taught Me." *Forbes Magazine.* May 5, 2015. Accessed May 9, 2016. http://www.forbes.com/sites/kathy-caprino/2014/05/05/4-life-changing-concepts-arianna-huffington-taught-me/2/#3210 51dd655b